A Day in th...
Axel the Ant

2ⁿᵈ Edition

I love reading! This book belongs to

_____

This book was received on the date below:

_____

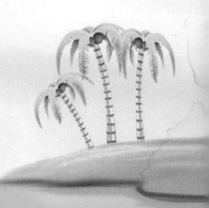

Publisher's Notes

It is noted that 'Engineer Greg' is the pseudonym of Gregory S. Skeete

Written by: Gregory Skeete a.k.a. Engineer Greg
Illustrated by: Gregory Skeete, Abira Das, Laura Garcia
Published by: Pilly Pelican Inc.
Website: www.pillypelican.com

Revised Second (2nd) Edition (September 2016)
Paperback Edition
ISBN-13: 9789769568877
Hardback Edition
ISBN-13: 9789769568860
E-book Editions
ISBN-13: 9789769610712 (ePub)
       9789769610729 (Mobi)
       9789769610736 (PDF)
Also available in Spanish and Dutch translations.
Other Editions:
DVD Videobook, Audiobook

Notes:
1st Edition ISBN-13: 978-1492120537 (September 2, 2013)

Also by the Author:
Milk Making - The Magic of Milk on the Moo-ooove from Grass to Glass
The Sweet Work of Bees
Easy Bee Productivity

Register Your Book

www.pilly.net/BookRegister

Contents

Words, Imagination and a Tropical Island

Reading is one of the most important skills to develop in life because you will need it for everything that you will do and all that you will ever learn. Even though my profession is engineering, and I work with many numbers and calculations, reading and writing are both equally as important to my success.

Reading can take you to places that you have never been and open doors that you had never imagined. When I was a child, I never dreamed that I would become the published author that I am now and it all started with this book!

Speaking of imagination, this book will take you on an entertaining, educational adventure as you learn about the beautiful island of Barbados. The story follows Axel, the hard-working, engineering ant, and his pal, Pilly the Pelican, during a typical day of Axel's life in his tropical paradise.

I extend thanks to my writing coach and editor, Linda M. Deane, who provide essential, professional feedback in the making of one of Barbados' favourite children's books.

To my family in Barbados and around the world, I dedicate this to you. I am thankful for the continued love and support which you have given over the years in so many ways.

Finally, I dedicate the book to YOU, the reader!

I hope you enjoy this story and learn from Axel's good habits. I also encourage you to never stop learning and to always do your best. Remember, readers are leaders!

ENGINEER GREG

A Day In The Life Of
Axel The Ant

by Engineer Greg

Hello, little friend,
how do you do?

I'm Pilly the
Pelican—it's
good
to see you!

I live in the
Caribbean,
in sunny
Barbados.

Flying over the
island is what
I love most.

One day,
while flying over
the trees and the
plants,

I looked down
and saw my
friend Axel
the Ant.

I said, "Hello, Mr. Ant, what do you do each day?"

Axel said, "Sometimes I work, and sometimes I play!"

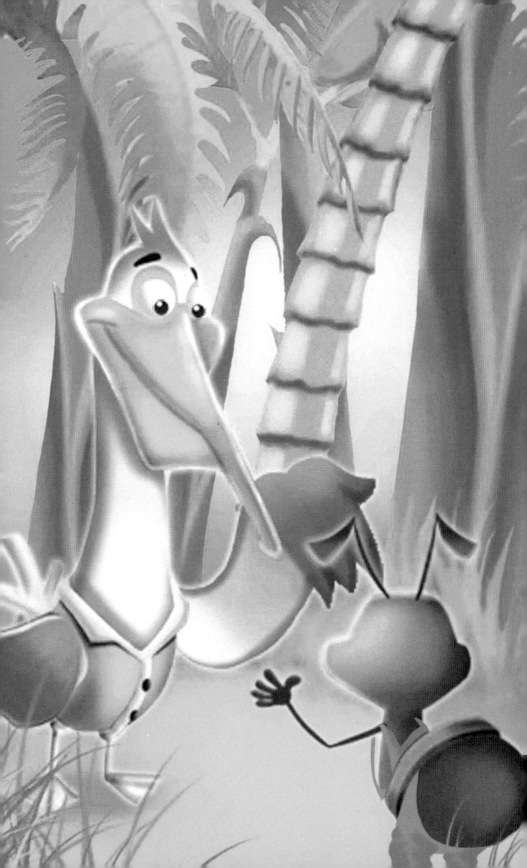

"Axel, my friend,
I would sure
love to see."

"Sure, Pilly
Pelican—just
follow me!

14

I start
each day at
6 o'clock by
gathering food
to eat.

I like bananas
and mangoes—
and anything
that's sweet!

I love to look
at the colourful
flowers and
the big trees.

When I'm there,
I always say hello
to the bees!

We ants are very small, but we are super strong!

We can lift objects that are HEAVY, BIG and LONG.

After lifting all that
fruit, sometimes
I feel tired.

But I have to
get to work on
time so I don't get
fired!

I'm at work by 8 o'clock, so there is never any panic.

I love my job of fixing cars – I'm a great mechanic!

At 12 o'clock,
I go to lunch,
which I can't wait
to take.

My favourite lunch
is Bajan 'fishcakes
and bakes'!

TODAY'S SPECIAL

Fish cakes & Bakes

12:30

After lunch,
it's back to work
fixing all those
cars.

I feel good at
leaving time,
knowing I've
worked hard.

After work, there's a place that I am happy to reach.

If you live in Barbados, you must go to the beach!

I love the
warm sun and the
coconut trees,

and I cannot
forget the
sweetest
sea-breeze.

It's hot, but not too far to roam...

in search of a sweet, ice-cold sno-cone.

SNO-CONE

And when
the beach gets
even hotter—

It's fun to
splash in cool
seawater!

There, we'll
see my friend
called Flo—

with her beautiful
flying fish wings
on show.

After the beach,
it's home
for dinner.

Yum!
Cou-cou makes
me feel like a
winner!

After eating
all of those sweets,
my teeth
I must brush.

I clean them
carefully, and
I am sure
not to rush.

At bedtime,
I always
read a book.

Then I'm
fast asleep before
you can look!"

Comprehension Activities

Think and answer the questions below:

1. What are the names of the pelican and ant in the story?
2. In which country does the story take place?
3. What time does Axel begin collecting fruits?
4. What fruits do Axel and Pilly lift in the story?
5. What time does Axel get to work?
6. Where does Axel work?
7. What is the Barbadian meal eaten by Axel and Pilly at lunch time?
8. What does Axel drink at the beach?
9. Who is Flo?
10. Axel eats a special meal for dinner. What is it called?
11. In the picture on Page 41, at what time does Axel eat dinner?
12. Name two (2) things which Axel does before going to sleep at night.

Creative Activities

Imagine, Draw and Colour!

1. Draw the national flag of Barbados.

2. Draw the map of Barbados.

3. Draw a picture of Axel the Ant collecting mangoes.

4. Draw a picture of Pilly the Pelican flying in the sky.

5. Draw a picture of Flo the Flying-fish under-water.

6. Draw pictures of your favourite fruits and foods.

7. Draw ten clocks to show the following times:

   - 8:00, 10:30, 12:00, 2:30, 4:00
   - 7:15, 9:45, 12:30, 3:15, 6:00

Imagine and Write!

8. Write a story about what you do in a day of your life.

9. Write a story saying what you do at the beach.

10. Axel the Ant loves Barbadian fruits and food. Write a story about your favourite fruits and foods.

Facts & Teaching Guide

Children ask plenty of questions—especially when reading picture books. When I was a boy, on every page I would be asking "And Mum, what's that?" or "Why is that flower that colour?"

Mindful of this, I've included the following short teaching section to help answer questions children or adults might have while reading *A Day in the Life of Axel the Ant*. It contains facts and general knowledge about the "Gem of the Caribbean Sea", as Barbados is affectionately known. Important points are in bold. Enjoy!

10 Facts About Barbados

1. Barbados **(Page 9)** is the most **eastern island** of the chain of islands located in the **Caribbean Sea**. It looks like Africa turned upside down. It is relatively small country, as it measures only **166 miles²** or **430 km²**. Barbados can fit into the USA about **22,800 times** and has an approximate population of **290,000 people**.

2. Barbados has **4 towns** and **11 parishes**. The capital is called **Bridgetown**, and is located in the parish of **St. Michael**. There was once a small land mass called **Pelican Island** located just off the coast of Bridgetown. It was called Pelican Island because of the many brown pelicans that nested there. Between 1956 and 1961, the land between Bridgetown and Pelican Island was reclaimed when the Bridgetown Port was being constructed. Pelican Island is now a part of the **'Deep Water Harbour'** in Bridgetown.

3. A **pelican** appears with a **dolphin** on the Barbados **Coat of Arms**. These two animals are iconic to the island, along with the **flying fish** as characterized by **'Flo'** on **Page 39**.

4. The flower shown on **Page 19** with the honeybee is a national emblem, which is also found on the Barbados Coat of Arms. A beautiful and exotic flower, it is known as **"The Pride of Barbados"** and is gold and red-orange in colour.

5. The lunchtime meal Axel the Ant is eating on **Page 27** is called **fishcakes and bakes**. It is a very popular, fried snack in Barbados. Fishcakes are made from a salt-fish batter, and the bakes are made from flour dough.

6. The dinner of **cou-cou** Axel enjoys on **Page 41** is part of the **National Dish of Barbados**. It consists mainly of cornmeal (corn flour) and okras but can be made from breadfruit or green bananas. In Barbados, it is normally eaten with flying fish as a delicacy. However, this does not apply to our friend Flo! ☺

7. Although small, Barbados has one of the **highest literacy rates** in the world. This is mainly because education was made free under the leadership of **Barbados' first Prime Minister, The Right Excellent Errol Walton Barrow**.

8. People who live in Barbados are known as **Barbadians** or **'Bajans'**. 'Bajan' also refers to the local dialect of the island, which is a form of broken English that is spoken rather quickly.

9. In the national flag of Barbados shown on **Page 9**, the **blue panels** represent **the sea** and **the sky**. The inner **yellow panel**

represents the beautiful **golden sand**. The **black Trident** in the centre of the flag is the mythical trident of **the sea god Neptune**. It is **broken** to represent **independence** from **England** which occurred on **November 30th, 1966**, after the British first landed on Barbadian shores in 1625, and settled in 1627.

10.The **Bearded Fig Tree** shown on **Page 15** is also an emblem appearing in the centre of the Coat-of-Arms of Barbados. The name Barbados comes from the **Portuguese** word **'los barbados'** which means **'Bearded One'**. This is because the island was covered with these bearded fig trees when the first European settlers arrived.

I hope you enjoyed learning about Barbados. As a souvenir, here's a photo overlooking Barbados' East Coast from Cherry Tree Hill.

Connect With Pilly!!!

Thank You

From the sunny shores of Barbados, we would like to extend a warm Caribbean greeting and thank you for 'Reading with Pilly'! Our books combine the ideal mix of children's entertainment and education. We hope you and your little ones enjoyed it and that it has added value with lots of questions, laughs and smiles.

Join Our Community

We love to connect with the parents and adults who invest and contribute to the growth and development of children. We are building a community of people who are committed to making future generations better. We want to know which books you have and which you love.

If you have purchased or used this book with the children or students in your life, we would like you to register it online. You will then be able to receive the latest updates, events, behind the scenes information, previews, parenting tips and even help us determine what topics our future books should be about!

Readers who have registered their book will also receive future discounts, free gifts and giveaways as they occur. It's quick and as easy as 1-2-3!

Register Your Book

www.pilly.net/BookRegister

Tell Us What You Liked

We love to hear what readers like about our books. Please visit our website or **www.pilly.net/Review** to leave a review and share your experience with us!

More Pilly The Pelican Books

Milk Making - The Magic of Milk on the Moo-ooove from Grass to Glass

Find out what happens when Pilly the Pelican meets Bert the Bull and they explore the magic of milk on the moo-ooove through the dairy process in 'Milk Making'!

This book has been designed to teach children about milk from a holistic perspective which includes the science and engineering processes at the farm and the factory before reaching the cups of the consumers.

Children will learn the answers to these questions and much more!

- Where does milk come from?
- What is the process for producing milk?
- What equipment is used to make milk?
- What and how much do cows eat?
- How much do cows weigh?
- What insects affect cows?
- How often do farmers milk cows?
- How is milk transported from place to place?
- How much milk do cows make each day?
- How long can milk last?
- What are the health benefits of drinking milk?
- What is the composition of milk?
- What other products are made from milk?
- What types of micro-organisms exist in milk?

Made in the USA
Las Vegas, NV
09 February 2021

17479132R00033